ENERGY

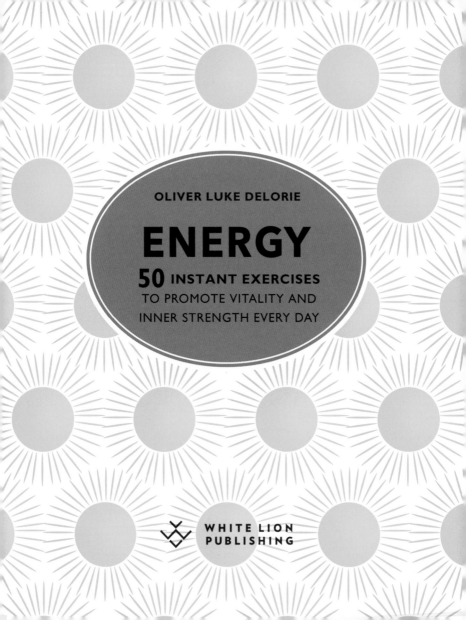

OLIVER LUKE DELORIE

ENERGY

50 INSTANT EXERCISES
TO PROMOTE VITALITY AND
INNER STRENGTH EVERY DAY

WHITE LION
PUBLISHING

Inspiring | Educating | Creating | Entertaining

Brimming with creative inspiration, how-to projects and useful information to enrich your everyday life, Quarto Knows is a favourite destination for those pursuing their interests and passions. Visit our site and dig deeper with our books into your area of interest: Quarto Creates, Quarto Cooks, Quarto Homes, Quarto Lives, Quarto Drives, Quarto Explores, Quarto Gifts, or Quarto Kids.

First published in 2020 by White Lion Publishing,
an imprint of The Quarto Group.
The Old Brewery, 6 Blundell Street,
London, N7 9BH,
United Kingdom
T (0)20 7700 6700
www.QuartoKnows.com

© 2020 Quarto Publishing plc.

QUAR.333797

Project Editor: Anna Southgate
Designer: Dave Jones
Art Director: Gemma Wilson
Publisher: Samantha Warrington

A catalogue record for this book is available from the British Library.

ISBN 978 17813 1977 2

Ebook ISBN 978 1 78131 978 9

10 9 8 7 6 5 4 3 2 1

Printed in China

MIX
Paper from
responsible sources
FSC® C008047

CONTENTS

INTRODUCTION

Every dictionary definition of energy focuses on its dynamic and active nature, and its capacity for producing a variety of results in various forms, some of which are covered in this book. Invest your time and energy in these 50 mindful exercises, and you will be confidently roused into conscious, creative effort so dynamic in nature that you will get results.

Everything is made of energy. By learning to harness, generate and channel it, you are in essence learning to alter your perception of reality and to perceive it more clearly. The art and science of energy 'engineering' can blow your mind, for the benefits and results can be intoxicating. This collection of physical, emotional and spiritual processes endeavours to engage, enlighten and empower you to master possibly the only truly meaningful occupation in your life. A tall order, no doubt, but what could be more valuable or meaningful than learning how to cooperate with the source of everything you see, feel, taste, touch, smell and intuit?

What is required? A delicate mix of passion, perspective, patience and persistence. Everyone dances within the duality of nature in every nanosecond – both consciously and unconsciously – for managing emotional energy sounds simple, but is not easy. We are taught how (and how not) to express our emotions before we can even talk. In our early years caregivers express and unconsciously project their emotions towards us. This can result in instances of miscommunication on a deep psychological level that imprints our brains with emotional responses we have a difficult time controlling, especially when under pressure. But we can cope – and change, even – by practising these exercises either alone, with a trusted friend or with professional help.

Physically, we are battery-powered engines buzzing with energy. Our cells are conductors of currents that pulse with electrically charged ions generated by elements such as sodium, calcium and magnesium. They allow our nervous system (which requires electricity) to send signals to the brain and body so we can think, feel and move.

Spiritually speaking, think of energy as an invisible force flowing in and out and through everything that exists. Metaphysically (beyond the tangible, physical world of matter), every square-nano-sized space of formlessness is alive with ethereal, intangible spirit that 'energy workers' of all disciplines are able to sense and direct towards various faith-based and divine 'energy-healing' purposes.

These 50 exercises will energize you in three ways. They will help you manage your emotions; they will guide you in channelling your physical energy towards creative/productive/healthy pursuits; and they will put a spring back in your soul's step. Drawing on mindfulness-based stress reduction (MBSR), emotional brain training (EBT) and cognitive behavioural training (CBT), practising the exercises will help you transcend negative thought patterns, enabling your self-esteem to soar as you create a better world for yourself and for the people you care about most.

When to seek help

Many hurdles to personal and professional success can be swiftly overcome with information, processes and a playful nudge. Books like this are useful in providing such guidance, but if you find your negative emotions are affecting your health, your relationships or your career, please consult with a professional.

TEN WAYS ENERGY CAN HELP YOU

Focusing on energy can change your attitude and enhance your life in all kinds of ways. Here are some of the benefits:

1 Increased energy activates your immune system, making you feel healthier.

2 A restful sleep makes you more productive and creative.

3 A boost of energy helps you find more enjoyment in the activities you enjoy partaking in.

4 You can reduce the amount of physical pain you may feel.

5 You'll be motivated to follow through with your goals and dreams.

6 You'll be less prone to depression, stress and anxiety.

7 Being energized has been proven to establish new neural networks in the brain.

8 It increases your satisfaction with your relationships.

9 It brings about a sense of awe and wonder.

10 It makes you feel as if life is worth living.

Cognitive behavioural therapy (CBT)

Often referred to as CBT, cognitive behavioural therapy is a preferred method of psychotherapy. Its tools and processes can quickly lead to new insights and effect lasting change by clarifying your challenges and helping you respond to life in an enduring way. Even though you risk discomfort when dealing with distress from the past, everyone (regardless of their mental wellbeing) will find value in CBT, because developing strategies to better cope with and manage the stress in one's life are skills from which everyone can benefit.

Mindfulness-based stress reduction (MBSR)

The definition of mindfulness is focusing only on what is happening in each moment and letting go of thoughts about the past or the future. Reducing stress in a mindful way is not about zoning out or spacing out; rather it is an opportunity to intentionally pay attention to what is happening both inside and outside of your body simultaneously. By becoming aware of your thoughts, feelings, surroundings and environment, you will soon realize the temporary nature of everything; how fleeting life itself (and everything in it) is.

MBSR is especially effective when you are feeling stressed out. What better time to get in touch with what's really bothering you, so you can become acquainted with it, and maybe even understand where the sensations are coming from? You never know, you may even feel empowered enough to let it go after a quiet, contemplative session of emotionally detached analysis.

How to use this book

This book provides numerous ways to help you feel healthier and live with increased vitality. The methods and processes make it easy for you to open the book at random and try any exercise that appeals to you. Or feel free to work your way through chapter by chapter to capitalize on every kilowatt, volt and joule you can squeeze out of it.

Emotional brain training (EBT)

EBT is the idea that it's possible to confront the destructive patterns that keep us stuck in unhealthy diets, lifestyles and relationships by enabling us to experience unconditional self-acceptance and clarity of thought and purpose. Techniques involve rewiring the neural networks in your brain to prevent thoughts or feelings that instinctively compel you to fight, flee or freeze in certain situations.

Positive affirmations

Throughout this book are short phrases that you can repeat to yourself to gradually train the nonconscious part of your brain to focus on how it can help you achieve your goals by channelling your energy in the direction you want to go.

HEALTH IS
WEALTH

Without vibrant health, few things are possible. Maintaining physical, emotional and spiritual wellbeing is a simple goal, but not easy to attain or sustain. This chapter will help you become more conscious of how wellness can help you experience life in a new way.

Distractions such as watching TV, surfing the Internet and shopping put a strain on the nervous system, which is made up of two parts: the sympathetic and the parasympathetic. The sympathetic nervous system controls our 'fight, flight or freeze' response, while the parasympathetic is responsible for our 'rest and digest' mode. Given the stresses and distractions of daily living, most of us tend to live on what a doctor would refer to as 'sympathetic overdrive'.

Tap into the parasympathetic nervous system and embrace the calm, confident vibrations that induce happiness and lead to healing. In this way you can approach every encounter with cool, calm patience and will be ready to accept everything as it is.

GAUGE AND GO

Imagine you are a car tyre. When your air pressure is correct, you cruise along without a care in the world. But when life wears you down and deflates you, you lose time, money and energy. Finding balance is key: if you are too pressurized, you will feel every little stone in the road; run low, and you risk losing control. Use this visualization exercise to help you assess – and address – what is deflating (or overinflating) your inner tyres.

1 As with a tyre gauge, measure your energy level on a scale of −3 to +3, the former being a lower energy level and the latter a higher energy level. Now in your mind's eye, picture this registering on a thermometer-type gauge.

2 Now check for any holes. If so, where are they? What's draining your energy? Or if you feel full of (hot) air, what's the cause?

3 See if you can plug the holes you find, or otherwise release some energy in a positive way – like sweating it out with exercise or going for a brisk, short walk.

4 Moving forward, pledge to yourself that you will regularly balance the pressure in your tyres whenever you feel it's necessary. Affirmations such as 'I will not feel anxious' or 'Nobody's perfect' can help you with this.

WHEN TO DO IT

Practise this exercise at any time of the day or night when your energy levels start to wane and you want to rebalance your tyres.

ENERGY ENEMIES

Watch out for energy-draining emotions such as boredom, depression, perfectionism, addiction, anxiety, anger and obsessive thinking.

02 LONG-LIFE LAUGHTER

Consider a dose of laughter meditation medicine to kick you into a high gear! Perhaps the most significant benefit of laughing is the perspective it provides. You can't feel anxious, scared, stuck or lost while laughing out loud. Nor can feelings of anger, fear and hatred creep up behind you while you are simultaneously delighting in joy, pleasure and lightness of being. This laughter exercise is one of the easiest forms of meditation.

1 Start by stretching your body like a cat or dog waking up from a nap.

2 Stand with your feet shoulder-width apart for 1 to 2 minutes, arms raised above your head. Gently rock from side to side and then bend over to see if you can touch your toes. Give your jaw a gentle massage and yawn a few times to get your mouth ready for action.

3 Standing or sitting comfortably, crack a smile and chuckle lightly to yourself for 3 to 5 minutes. See if you can get your belly involved. Even if it feels forced at first, you will be enjoying yourself in no time. Once you've got your jollies out, sit or lie down on the floor and relax your body. How do you feel? What thoughts arise?

WHEN TO DO IT

This is a MUST whenever you have gone more than one day without laughing about something. Feel free to record your experiences in a journal or share them with a trusted friend.

03 EAT A RAISIN

Your body works on autopilot to convert food and drink into energy to keep you alive. Although we depend on food for fuel, we sometimes develop unconscious emotional relationships with our primary energy source. This mindfulness-based exercise is designed to help you experience the benefits of mindful eating. Not only will it help you resolve any difficulties, but also to appreciate what you put in your body every day. If you don't have a raisin, substitute any food you like.

1 Put the raisin (or alternative food) in your hand. Pretend you have travelled from a galaxy far, far away and have never had the pleasure of eating this food before. Ignore your parent's voice in your head saying, 'Don't play with your food' because that's exactly what you are going to do!

2 Act as if this is the first time you have ever seen this food. Turn it over and rouse every sense. What colour is it? What does it remind you of? Have you felt any texture or shape like this before?

3 If you happen to think 'Why am I doing this?' or 'How is this supposed to help me be more mindful?', just let these thoughts float away as quickly as they came, and return to focusing 100 per cent on the food in your hand.

4 Now slowly bring the food up to your nose and smell it. What images or ideas or sensations does it conjure? Close your eyes if you find it helps you focus.

5 Hold the food beside your ear. Squeeze it and move it around a little. If it's not generally a noisy food, try to get it to make a sound if you can.

WHEN TO DO IT

Try this when you catch yourself running on autopilot and taking your senses for granted. Just pause and practise mindful eating to reconnect with your food.

6 Now place the food on your tongue, but don't bite it yet. What do your tastebuds say? Are you aware of any texture or initial taste?

7 When you are ready to bite the food, notice how it moves around in your mouth. Try to chew it slowly and notice any taste the food releases as you do so. As the food mixes with your saliva, pay attention to its consistency as it changes.

8 Swallow the food when you are ready. Notice it moving down your throat on its way to your stomach. As it makes its journey, quietly acknowledge that it is providing you with a natural form of wholefood energy.

KEEP A RECORD

Make a note of what happens each time, so you can look back over your findings. See if your experience changes with the foods you try.

MINDFUL EATING JOURNAL

Use this page to record your impressions and reflections.

Type of food:

How did it look?

How did it feel?

What did it smell like?

How did it sound?

What did it taste like?

Did anything surprise you?

What thoughts or memories arose during your experience?

RAIN ON YOUR BRAIN

When you're feeling overwhelmed, your brain filling with the opposite of positive, constructive, life-affirming vibes, try this cognitive behavioural therapy exercise to avoid thoughts that sap your energy. We are so hard on ourselves and create so much unnecessary stress. This wonderful exercise will free you up from negative thinking, teach you how to see things in a simple, unattached way and perk you up so you can get on with your life.

WHEN TO DO IT

Slip into this way of thinking every time you are faced with a difficult situation. Remember the four letters of this creative cognitive exercise and let love and acceptance rain on your brain.

1 The next time you feel on the brink of negativity, remember the acronym R.A.I.N.
R: Recognize. What is actually happening? How are you reacting to the situation?

2 A: Allow. Let the experience be what it is. Pause and pay attention. Pretend you are having an out-of-body experience, or that you are hovering above it all in a helicopter, just watching.

3 I: Interest. Make kind and careful enquiries. What am I believing about this? What is true? Try not to judge your thoughts or feelings.

4 N: Nonidentification. Simply notice whatever is happening, name it ('I feel hurt' or 'I am scared'). Now let it be, let it go and be free.

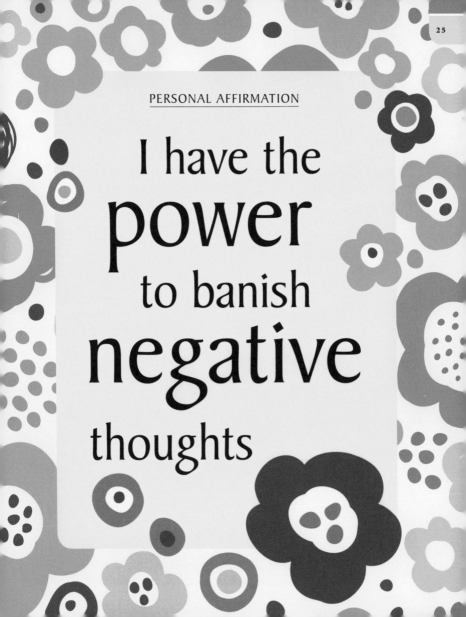

PERSONAL AFFIRMATION

I have the power to banish negative thoughts

05 DECAFFEINATED

If Coffee is your closest friend and you can't seem to make it through the day without spending time together, it might be time for a little intervention. Caffeine doesn't give you more energy; it blocks the adenosine receptors in your body from getting the adenosine they normally do, and this reduces the amount of fatigue you feel. You may feel energized, but this inhibits your ability to correctly assess your energy levels. Try this visualization exercise to help find balance in your relationship.

1 Warmly thank Coffee for being such a dear companion over the years.

2 Acknowledge the positive feelings you experience when you get together and then calmly let Coffee know that 'it's not you, it's me'. Coffee will likely not understand this, and may become defensive.

3 If you and Coffee have been meeting three times a day, suggest you reduce it to just once a day, but for a little longer each time (quality is more important than quantity).

4 Once Coffee has come to terms with your new relationship, decide you will find central nervous system stimulation in other ways so that you may achieve a harmonic balance within yourself and with your environment.

5 If you do not succeed in kicking your habit the first time, simply repeat steps 1 to 4. See if you can summon the courage to confront Coffee the next time you are stirred into action.

WHEN TO DO IT

Practise this exercise whenever you feel energized to achieve mind-body-spirit alignment.

06 REALITY CHECK

Most intoxicants are designed to deaden or enliven your experience of life. Understanding why and how you self-medicate will help you refocus the energy you expend on escaping reality. Alcohol is the most commonly used recreational drug, so it is the focus of this mindfulness-based exercise. But take care: imbibing too much can make it difficult to discern between an educational experience and the alternative. Do not plan to drive afterwards.

1 Pour yourself an alcoholic drink, sit down and take a few deep breaths. Feel the air entering and leaving your nose at the base of your nostrils.

2 Relax. Continue to breathe for ten minutes before taking a sip of your drink. Notice any thoughts and feelings of anticipation and/or avoidance. What are you seeking? What are you trying to escape?

3 Once you feel calm, have a drink. Imbibe enough to change your state of awareness, but not so much that it interferes with your ability to pay attention. Notice both the pleasant and unpleasant effects of the alcohol and be with them.

WHEN TO DO IT

Try this if you want a positive relationship with addictive, intoxicating substances – one that allows you to make informed decisions when it comes to channelling your attention and resources into alternative pursuits that spice up your life.

TOP **FIVE** WAYS
to heal your body

Slow down and be present

Play and have fun

Eat foods that energize you

Dance, stretch, bend and jump!

Release destructive emotions

07 GET ON THE FLOOR

Developed in India thousands of years ago, yoga began as a sitting meditation, but when the meditators got stiff and sore, they began paying attention to how the animals around them seemed to benefit from stretching and moving around. The meditators began copying the animals' movements and noticed their bodies became stronger and more flexible. Today, many yoga poses are named after animals and are designed to maintain your energy levels so you can be more productive.

1 Lie down on your back with your arms at your sides, palms facing up and breathing naturally. Breathe in and sweep your arms up over your head with your palms facing each other. Exhale and bring your arms back down to your sides.

2 Sweep your arms out to shoulder height. Now bend your knees and raise them up, keeping your feet on the floor, then move them to one side while looking in the opposite direction. Keep breathing, and repeat on the other side.

3 Stretch your legs out again, then bring your arms back to your sides. Raise your right leg, point your heel to the ceiling, then lower it slowly to the floor. Repeat with your left leg.

4 Keeping your left leg straight, bring your right knee to your chest. Breathe, being mindful of any sensations you feel. Repeat with your left knee.

WHEN TO DO IT

Practise this calm routine every morning or night to gently stretch your body. Wear comfortable clothing.

PERSONAL AFFIRMATION

May I
love
what
comes

08 LOVE YOURSELF TO SLEEP

We are often so full of energy that we have difficulty sleeping; we find ourselves tossing and turning, our minds buzzing with past histories and future mysteries; we buy fancy mattresses and drug ourselves, but still find no relief. Research has shown the better you sleep, the more energy you have available for the people, places and things that matter during the day. Quell anxiety and insomnia and metaphorically put your inner tigers to sleep by practising this loving kindness exercise tonight (and every night) before bed, and you will wake up revitalized.

1 Think of your bed as a place of rest, a sanctuary for sleeping or a cosy cocoon for your nightly catnap. Darken your room and get comfortable.

2 Close your eyes, take a deep breath and slowly, silently repeat to yourself, 'May I be happy, may I be peaceful, may I be forgiving, may I learn to let go, may I love what comes'.

3 You may find that learning to love yourself is quite difficult. If so, remember that resistance to inwardly-focused loving kindness is futile. You will eventually break down the walls that keep you separate from what you love.

WHEN TO DO IT

Try this relaxing, loving exercise every night when you get into bed. Once you have been practising for a while, you may feel more relaxed and find you don't need as much sleep. Some experts believe this may be due to the fact that your need for restorative sleep has been met by your mindfulness meditation.

09 FIND THE GOOD

We would all like to live more fulfilling and more exhilarating lives; we daydream about being more creative, successful, adored and celebrated. But as we focus on becoming better human beings and concentrate on imaginary futures, we lead ourselves away from appreciating what is happening right here, right now. Why look for solutions to your 'problems' in places you may never find them? This exercise will help instil gratitude for the good things in life, and allow you to build a solid foundation of self-esteem that will put your inner battery on a trickle-charger so you always have the power to make your dreams come true.

1 Every night before you go to bed, think of five things you enjoyed about your day, and what caused the five things to turn out as they did.

2 Remember that what you focus on, you will continue to focus on, for the thoughts and feelings you entertain can't help but take shape in your life in one form or another.

3 By reflecting on the good things that happen to you every day, you are actually training yourself to find the positive in every situation. When this becomes a habit, you will notice you aren't sweating the small stuff as much as you used to.

WHEN TO DO IT

Do this every night before you fall asleep and your nonconscious brain will seek out more of the same.

10 STEP INTO SADNESS

Are you afraid of the dark? Or your feelings? Minding our emotional wellbeing keeps us from getting stuck in depression and despair just as cognitively connecting the dots between thoughts and emotions has the power to energize us with feelings that we have unlimited potential. Cognitive behavioural experts encourage separating rational from irrational thoughts – and obviously favour the former – so that we can more easily identify automatic negative thoughts (called ANTs). Give this exercise a try and see if you can exorcise these ANTs from your inner picnic so you can eat (and party) in peace.

1 If you are feeling depressed, close your eyes and remember the last time you felt good. What were you thinking at the time? Reminisce about how wonderful your life looked, and what you were imagining about the future.

2 If you are feeling good, close your eyes and recall the last time you felt depressed. What were you thinking? Was the depression triggered by a single event or did the feelings grow slowly over time? How did you feel about your future? Perhaps that things were never going to get better?

WHEN TO DO IT

Do this exercise when you find yourself submerged in sadness or are ecstatically excited about something.

3 Moods change faster than the weather, and with each shift come different thoughts. The problem is we sometimes feel as if the feelings won't pass, and that we'll always feel like this. But this isn't true. Thoughts aren't reality; thoughts are only our perception of reality.

4 Going back to steps 1 and 2, where did you feel these emotions in your body? See if you can pinpoint an area quite precisely.

5 What are the emotions that tend to show up regularly? And which ones are missing? Are there some emotions you consistently try to ignore or get rid of?

6 By paying attention to the flowing feelings and torrent of thoughts we have each day, you won't get knocked off balance as much as you did when you were sleepwalking with your eyes open.

WRITE IT DOWN

Keep a record of your experiences using the log opposite, and rating the intensity of the emotion on a scale of one to ten.

SELF-REFLECTION LOG

Event:

Emotion: Intensity

Reaction:

Event:

Emotion: Intensity

Reaction:

Event:

Emotion: Intensity

Reaction:

Event:

Emotion: Intensity

Reaction:

CREATIVE CONFIDENCE

New hobbies and activities wait patiently to inspire and energize you. The exercises in this chapter will entrust you with the skills and confidence to create anything you want in life, and to dance with whatever is. The creative confidence you earn will put you in the driver's seat of your life, while keeping you safe at every turn.

No judgement. No anxiety. No fear. As you celebrate and connect the celestial and earthly powers that be, you become a co-creator, an originator, a builder of the present and of the future. There is no greater power (nor responsibility) than harnessing your inner genius. Learn how to become focused on the task at hand and allow your intuition to lead you into and out of places you haven't visited before.

Be patient. Be daring. Be bold. Begin. In your creative practice you will be encouraged to forget, and then to learn again. You will be guided to soak up every drop of divine discovery so that you may bask in the humble glory of life blossoming into being in every moment made up of millions of milliseconds.

11 JUMP IN

Facing fear and turning it into courage is an enormous challenge, but the results can be energizing and empowering. Everyone feels fear, and until you learn how to see it for what it is (and muster the courage to deal with any troubles), you will feel debilitated, powerless and haunted. The more you practise, the less you will want to run and hide under the covers, praying for the big, bad wolf to go and blow someone else's house down. Use this emotional brain training exercise to help you take the plunge.

1 Accept whatever is troubling you, because no matter how hard you believe that becoming big, strong, rich, creative or successful will defeat it, fear never goes away.

2 Be honest with yourself. Acknowledge when you're afraid and see these times as opportunities to familiarize yourself with fear and learn how to overcome it.

3 Feel it (instead of trying to think your way out of, or through it). Analyzing or resisting doesn't diminish it; fearful feelings only persist. Get to know your apprehension. Have a conversation with it. Ask 'What can you teach me?'.

4 Face it. If you run away, it will continue chasing you. But turn and face it and you will see it isn't such a scary monster after all. Shine the light on it and a shadow evaporates.

5 Practise confronting the things that scare you. Just like you learned how to tie your shoes, ride a bike or learn to swim, the more you practise these steps, the more fear won't step on your toes.

WHEN TO DO IT

Mastering this skill will help you overcome obstacles. Just because no one taught you how to summon courage and trounce your fears doesn't let you off the hook. What's the worst that can happen? Jump in!

12 PHOTO SCAVENGER HUNT

When you look at something through a camera lens, you naturally focus intensely on what you see. Your brain calculates the quality of light, space, depth of field, colour and distance in nanoseconds without you even being conscious of what's happening. Concentrating your attention on the matter filling your viewfinder is a practice in presence and patience. This exercise will force you out of your comfort zone by lulling your mental barriers into submission, sparking your imagination and fuelling you with passion for capturing the essence of the energetic world around you.

1 The first rule of a photo scavenger hunt is: there are no rules.

2 Take a photo of a street sign or shop sign written in another language.

3 Take a photo of a food or ingredient you have yet to try.

4 Take a photo of a plant or flower that is beautiful to you.

5 Take a photo embodying what you believe to be the essence of creativity.

WHEN TO DO IT

Once a month. Photography is a window through which new insights come into focus. You learn that things aren't always as they appear.

GEAR AND GADGETS

You don't need fancy gear or gadgets to capture the essence of life around you, nor do you need any special skills or professional qualifications. Just play!

13 CROWD STORMING

The ability to create something out of nothing is not the reserve of creative geniuses, for everyone creates all sorts of stuff out of nothing every day. Everything you see either came into form in a galactic/cosmic/invisible/spiritual/holy way, or a human being fashioned it out of thin air (as in an idea, a poem or a song) or out of various materials they found lying around in the junk drawer or at the flea market. Everyone (including you) is a creative genius and two heads are usually better than one. Use this exercise to stimulate your next free flow of ideas so you can zip, zing, zig and zag your way to wherever you want to go.

1 Get a small group of friends together for breakfast, lunch or dinner – somewhere that will tolerate you if you get rowdy. Try to round up people with diverse interests and/or personalities who have different interests and careers.

2 Order some pizzas or ask each person to contribute some food and drink. The object of the game is to let people know you won't just be hanging out and socializing.

3 Let everyone know what you're working on, and where you're getting stuck. Then actually listen to what people have to say (and take notes). People will quickly get into the groove and ideas will start bouncing off the walls.

4 All ideas (even the improbable ones) are valid, for you never know where a train of thought is headed. Focus on each person, each moment and every concept to keep the flow of energy moving, always listening and paying attention.

WHEN TO DO IT

Try this when you can't see the direction you (or your project or plan or idea) want to go. Gatherings like this can become so popular, don't be surprised if it turns into a weekly event.

MUST HAVES

Make sure you have food and a space where everyone can relax. These two ingredients will ensure everyone has a good time.

14 ZERO POINT EMAIL

Free your mind so you can think more clearly and make more time for mindful meditations and inspired mind-body-spirit pursuits that align with feeling alive, more connected and energized. If you are like most people, your email inbox is full of other people's agendas all competing for your attention and draining your energy. See if you can liberate yourself from some of this excess 'paperwork'.

1 Think of your inbox as having three categories: messages you no longer need, messages you may need to refer back to in the future and messages requiring your attention.

2 Delete everything in category one. You don't need to hang on to spam or any messages whose time has expired. Stuff everything from category two into a folder system so that it's no longer in your inbox.

3 As for messages in category three, move them on to a to-do list of your choosing. Inbox empty at last! This takes energy and attention, but once complete, you will have exponentially more energy and be on your way to achieving a lasting Zen state of emptiness and clarity.

WHEN TO DO IT

When you no longer know what a serene state of clarity feels like, it's time to declutter your inbox. By doing so you will also declutter your mind.

QUICK FIX

Unsubscribe to any email newsletters that you never open, let alone read. And from now on, make a habit of opting out of opting in.

15 IMPROVIZE

Scientists define creativity as 'producing something new and useful'.
When they apply neuroscience to the creative process, they see the
proverbial spark most alive and active when the networks in our brains
are in balance, as creativity 'seems to require both freedom and constraint'.
When creating or improvizing, we are making things up as we go along,
so practise this mindful approach to creating something out of nothing,
and you will become turbo-charged. It's that easy.

1 Prepare to be creative. Think freestyle jazz. Mindfulness meditation increases your capacity for divergent thinking, so gently quiet your cognitive control network (turn off your autopilot) because you want your imagination to run wild.

2 Either pretend you are back in kindergarten or you are Michelangelo – however you like, stir your pot of potential. Make a mess. Get dirty. Think random thoughts. If your brain is busy buzzing like a bee from flower to flower, you may fly right by the hive, so stay focused and go with the ebb and flow.

3 Before you know it, your salience network (the part of your brain called the anterior midcingulate cortex), which detects the ripples of genius floating beneath the surface of your endless ocean of consciousness, will bless you with a stream of new ideas.

4 When the flow begins to ebb, log off and let your brilliant-beyond-belief ideas simmer on low for a while. Take a break and have a nap, take a walk, go surfing or make a sandwich. Stay offline and unwind.

5 Now look at your ideas objectively. As you refine your insights and summations, pay attention to those notions that are the most divinely inspired (to you). Persevere and you will solve problems.

WHEN TO DO IT

Experts suggest practising this exercise as often as possible, so try putting on your mindfully creative thinking cap at least once a week (if not every day).

16 MINDFUL MOTION

As a mindful movement practice, dance is an expressive arts experience. Dance invites all to come as they are, permitting them to leave all else at the door and confidently step into a physical conversation with one's environment. Whether in a group setting or on your own, freely flitting and frolicking elegantly across the dance floor gives your mind and body something to focus on. Then your spirit can channel a state of bliss so stimulating it can seem like time has stopped to watch you commune with the gods and goddesses of dance itself.

1 As always, your breath is where you are. Dance to music and see if you can feel the rhythmic qualities of your breath and heartbeat. Do they match? Can you synchronize the beat with both?

2 Listen only to the music. Let any lyrics guide you, as long as they don't distract you. Allow different parts of your body to imitate a different instrument or tone.

3 Your body has a mind of its own so let it move in ways it wants to. Remember to breathe. Do different parts of your body feel warm or cold? Which muscles love moving around? Which ones would rather stay sedentary?

WHEN TO DO IT

Whenever you feel the urge. You are welcome in your own body. You are free to express yourself however you wish. Dance for as long as you want and remember: no one is watching.

4 It may sound esoteric, but what stories does your body believe? What has your body known about life since you were born? For example, if your toes could talk, what would they say? Let the dance carry you away and you may find yourself with the permission to write a new story/belief into existence.

5 Are you self-conscious? The only one watching you is you! If you need to, create an imaginary bubble around yourself – one that no one can see through – and simply pretend you are alone. This is all about you.

6 When you allow your form to integrate with, and be influenced by, the two primary forces of energy (light and sound), you have ultimately created artistic fusion. Your gestures and expressive gesticulations have found their own pace and place in time and space, at which point you are now being 'danced', just as musicians often say they feel 'played' by music itself.

7 Now that you have awoken the healing power of both music and dance, pay attention to the ways in which your body changes over time, and observe how practice leads to perfection.

NEXT STEPS

You may also find you connect more deeply with other forms of creative expression, such as photography, writing, making music or cooking once you have found your footing in this fun art form. Experiment and improvize!

PERSONAL AFFIRMATION

I am light and sound

TOP **FIVE** WAYS
to energize your creativity

Use your imagination

Get some art or craft supplies, tools, instruments or materials

Leave your comfort zone and go somewhere you haven't been before

Inspiration is everywhere, you just have to find it

Ask questions

I always **clear** the **items** on my **to-do** list

17 JUST DO IT

Positive self-talk can motivate you, but when it's time to take action, that's what needs to happen. You hear 'just do it', but no one tells you how to 'just do it'. Use this exercise to help you get clear about what needs to get done, so you can start creating a life you love to live and feel the pride of accomplishment at the end of every day. Put off procrastination, and you will invite an energetic spring into your step.

1 Make a list of what you want (or need) to do. Include tasks to be completed today, this week, this month or this year. List as many things as you like, but not so many that you feel overwhelmed.

2 Prioritize each item based on when you would like (or need) to complete it. Break down each item into steps that you can check off as you complete them.

3 Keep track of the tasks you regularly complete to give you a better sense of how much time is required for similar tasks in the future.

4 How are you supposed to do this? Turn the page to find some strategies that will help you complete your tasks.

WHEN TO DO IT

Schedule the time and focus your energy. Create a blank calendar on a piece of paper or your computer and schedule your week in one-hour blocks of time. You will quickly see how many hours you have free.

PROCRASTINATOR BUSTER

Find the to-do list strategies that work best for you.

Worst first

Tackle the hardest task first. If you dread it, get it over with, and the rest will seem easy. This works well for something small, such as having a difficult telephone conversation.

Magic momentum

Start with something that excites you and gives you energy, and then use the momentum to keep going.

Just five minutes

Set your timer and spend five minutes on a task. Everyone can tolerate anything for a short length of time.

Prime time

Pick the best time of the day to do something. Perhaps you are naturally more productive in the morning or late at night.

Prime place

Certain rooms, spaces or environments are better suited to some tasks than others. Consider the task and 'feel out' the best place for you to work on it.

Set reminders

If you procrastinate because you forget things, use reminders to keep them top-of-mind. Write to-do lists or set up notifications on your phone.

Visualize it

You can often reduce the time or enormity of a task by working on it in your mind first. Try visualizing the task as if it's already completed, and imagine how you'll feel when it's done.

Get help

Ask a friend or family member to check in with you at an agreed upon time or stage of the process. Recruiting an accountability partner is effective.

Focus

If you are feeling distracted or unsettled, close your eyes and take a few deep breaths. This will calm you down and help you focus on getting to work and doing a good job.

Plan rewards

Celebrate when you have accomplished your goal(s). You will enjoy the rewards much more than if you skip dinner (the work) and go straight for dessert.

18 REWIND

Have you ever considered that sometimes the most appropriate way to move forwards is to go in the opposite direction? Do you find yourself running towards a brick wall (if not having already hit it) and consequently losing momentum and vitality? Not to mention the present-moment awareness that seems to instantly vanish when you are emotionally embedded in solving a problem? In this exercise, try starting from where you would ordinarily end and see how it goes.

1 Stop working on whatever you're doing, and spend the next 15 minutes attempting the opposite. If you are writing, start editing. If you are cutting, start gluing. Instead of drawing, start erasing. If you are frowning, smile.

2 If this is difficult, describe your process, system or approach to yourself in a few words, and then think of the antonym (the opposite).

3 Afterwards, document the internal and external struggles you faced (and perhaps overcame), reflecting on whether doing things counterintuitively excited or frightened you. What did you learn?

WHEN TO DO IT

Whenever you feel frustrated with slow progress. Whether you are keen for a quick experiment or you aim to innovate, rewinding the tape can unlock the gate to inventive new insight and give you a boost of energy.

19 ROLL THE DICE

Often the most random things that happen turn out to be the most inspiring and enjoyable. Enjoy some casual chaos every once in a while? Now is your chance. This exercise takes some guts, but the more mindful you are of the risks and rewards of this exercise, the more fun you will have. How will you know you are having fun? Because time will stand still, disarming your mind from entering into the equation at all. If you like your cosy rut, this electrifying exercise will encourage you to climb out of it and live a little, and maybe even flip a switch you didn't know you had.

1 Find (or make) three dice, each one of them numbered 1 to 6.

2 Create a list of 16 activities, adjectives, actions, foods, colours, people or places that appeal to you, and number them 3 to 18. (Each number corresponds to a possible roll of the three dice.)

3 Roll the dice and add their numbers together. What did they decide? Interpret them as you wish – the degree to which you excite/scare yourself is the degree to which you will feel energized.

4 Repeat at will and document the results so you have a record of your (mis)deeds.

WHEN TO DO IT

Do this when you haven't had a little excitement in longer than you can remember and want to spice things up.

CAUTION

Either you will play this game once or twice, have a giggle and forget all about it, or you will get addicted.

20 POETIC FOCUS

Spending time and energy dawdling around in fantasyland keeps you from living in the only place you exist: right here, right now. Having too many options in time and space at your disposal can be distracting and debilitating, carrying you (and your sense of vim and vigour) down the drain and even further away from what matters most to you. The point of this exercise is to help you see the gold nuggets patiently waiting to be dug up by learning to repurpose simple materials you use every day so you can not only conserve your energy, but also tap into new sources.

WHEN TO DO IT

If ever your mind is wandering its way around the detours in your brain on a lazy weekend, guide it towards this creative activity. Focus on the emotive meaning of each word as you carefully craft your contemplative yarns.

1 Choose a page in a magazine, newspaper, book or brochure (any document you don't mind altering) and look for words that seem to follow a theme, as if you were composing a poem.

2 Feel free to let your chosen document influence the words you choose, or simply follow your heart and your natural literary genius and let your innate sense guide you.

3 Circle or underline the words you choose and then grab a big felt-tip pen or load a paintbrush with paint and cover up all the other words on the page. Connect your selected words with arrows, shapes or frames, if you like.

FAVOURITE FRAGMENTS

Record your best efforts in the spaces below.

Document type:

Theme:

Fragment:

Document type:

Theme:

Fragment:

Document type:

Theme:

Fragment:

Document type:

Theme:

Fragment:

Document type:

Theme:

Fragment:

THE
DARK SIDE

We try not to think about it and we don't talk about it. We're not taught about it, nor do we believe in it, so to speak. The shadow isn't popular (which is why it's often referred to as the dark side), because who wants to shine a light on all their weaknesses and flaws? Stress, low self-esteem and lack of self-control can sap your energy, and so this chapter aims to help you acknowledge, appreciate and activate the positive aspects of the disowned traits of your personality.

These techniques will help you tap into the power of your nonconscious mind. They will encourage you to get dirty by digging into the neglected corners of your consciousness so you won't be tempted to turn to the dark side when Darth Vader inevitably offers his hand. There is no limit to what you can achieve, so change the bulb in your inner nightlight if it's burned out (and you've been too scared or lazy to replace it). Don't worry: your shadow isn't going anywhere; it has followed you around every day of your life and will still be there when you get back.

21 GIVE MONKEY A JOB

Neuroscientists estimate that while the nonconscious part of the brain is responsible for 95–98 per cent of what we do every day, we would explode if we had to consciously process it all at once. Thankfully, our subconscious brings only what's most relevant to our attention. Imagine this part of your brain is a monkey with unlimited energy; see if you can train your monkey to bring you the information, inspiration and encouragement you seek.

1 Retreat from the demands of your day and find a comfortable, quiet place to relax and take a few deep breaths. Ask yourself: if anything was possible, what could I be or do?

2 Clarify your goal and make it as specific as possible. Write it down, or repeat it to yourself until you get your hands on pen and paper. Turn it into an affirmation or mantra, and then brainwash your monkey to get to work and make it happen.

3 Keep track of your monkey. Egg it on every day by watching motivational videos or listening to energizing songs. If you want to lose weight, for example, put a picture of someone with the perfect weight on your desk and look at it every day. Monkey see, monkey do.

4 You are essentially training your monkey to train you. Put it to work and it will sift through the trillions of bits of information popping up around you all at once, and show you only the trail of breadcrumbs that leads to the top of the mountain.

WHEN TO DO IT

Once you have successfully completed the initial steps, continue training your monkey at every possible opportunity to stay focused on your goals.

PERSONAL AFFIRMATION

I open

myself

to love

22 A LIGHT HEART

We often ignore what our hearts say, and listen instead to the highbrow theories existing in our heads. We also know that negative emotions such as fear, anger and sadness shield and limit our heart's ability to give and receive feelings of happiness, kindness and love. Instead of ignoring your intuitive inner knowings and fraying the threads of your heartstrings, use this emotional brain training exercise to unlock the door to your centre and lead you forward with warm enthusiasm for new experiences.

1 Lie, sit or stand and close your eyes. Spend a few moments focusing on your heart. Feel it expand and contract with each breath. After about two minutes, check in. How does your heart feel now? Is it bigger? More relaxed?

2 Intention is powerful; it guides and directs our actions. By consciously choosing to feel the frequencies and vibrations of love, joy and compassion, you can foil frustration, fear and anxiety. Extend your arms and reach out for love.

3 When your hands are full, say 'I open myself to love', and bring your hands to your chest. Let the love soak into you, saying 'May love rest in my heart' (or whatever feels right to you).

WHEN TO DO IT

Frequently. There is no limit to the light of love, so you can put your faith and trust in the fact your cup will always be full.

23 UNDER PRESSURE

Ever find yourself stressed out because you're running late, or tensing up when things don't go according to your timetable? Ever lose your temper? Impatience impedes your life, sabotaging you from the murky shadows and leading to further frustration. If you can't accept delays and tolerate troubles, you become like a shaken bottle of fizz about to burst. Use this cognitive behavioural therapy exercise to transmute this effervescent energy into calm composure so you don't explode at any minute.

1 Check in with yourself to see if you're being impatient. Symptoms include: shallow breathing, muscle tension, restless feet or hands, irritability and anger, anxiety and nervousness and making snap/ quick decisions.

2 Now find the cause. What people, words or situations triggered you? Keep a journal and refer back to it regularly to see if patterns exist. Knowing what caused your frustrations may help steer you in a new direction next time.

3 Ask others if they know what winds you up. We have basic needs that don't always get met, which means sometimes you may just be hungry or thirsty. Fill up your water bottle.

4 If impatience persists, take deep, slow breaths and count to ten. See if you can mentally distance yourself from what's happening. Repeat if necessary, knowing you always have a choice as to how you react to any situation.

WHEN TO DO IT

Whenever you spot the symptoms listed in step 1. Let your inner bottle of fizz sit for a bit after you've shaken it up, and then open it slowly. Let life and other people move at their own speed, because you don't have any say in the matter.

24 JEDI MIND BEND

Like most people, you probably spend time thinking about how to be happier. Perhaps you even fear unhappiness, and this only wastes precious energy as you wallow in self-pity. This exercise, devised by psychologist Randy Paterson, is designed to help you stop making yourself miserable by starting to focus on what you need to turn your crank here, now, today, this minute, this second, by paradoxically focusing on what makes you miserable here, now, today, this minute, this second.

WHEN TO DO IT

This counterintuitive, mind-bending exercise can infuse your life with positive energy whenever the view from the treadmill is grim.

1 What would make you feel worse than you do right now? What drags you down? Becoming a couch potato? Eating junk food all day? Comparing yourself to other people? Make a list of everything you can think of that would make your life even more abysmal, and examine your motivations.

2 Now take a moment to consider how your daily habits are contributing to your unfortunate existence and experience how each affects you on various levels. Following inspection you may notice you are not too far gone or as defective as you thought. If your mood has lifted, celebrate!

3 Relish the opposite of each frightful flaw and ill-fated future trajectory.

MOOD-MAKING OPPOSITES

Try this mind-bending exercise. Use the column on the left to list five to ten personal traits and habits that drag you down. Then use the column on the right to suggest ways in which you can turn them from negatives to positives.

	Negative traits	Positive opposites
1		
2		
3		
4		
5		
6		
7		
8		
9		
10		

25 PULL WEEDS

Self-help gurus like to use the metaphor of how our subconscious minds are like gardens, and that we reap what we sow. While simple but not easy, this magically therapeutic exercise will eventually prove to you that the spirited life force suffusing all things beneath the surface of appearance requires nothing but your attentive attendance. Will you commit some energy to becoming a master gardener?

1 Choose your seeds carefully from life's seed catalogue and sprout them according to the instructions on the package.

2 Plant them in fertile soil in a sunny spot and water the tender shoots every day.

3 Pull the weeds that inevitably try to steal your shoots' resources and ultimately suffocate your 'precious' plants.

4 Be patient, do the necessary work and you will one day be blessed with a beautiful flower or vegetable that will inspire you to dig up even more of your lawn.

WHEN TO DO IT

As with other subtly subversive ways of producing something from nothing, you will start to see a shift in energy in as little as a month by investing 10 to 20 minutes a day weeding and watering the garden in your mind.

26 ANTI-KRYPTONITE

What is your kryptonite? What is lurking in the shadows sapping your energy and threatening to destroy you? Heavy stuff, no doubt, but no reason to seek sanctuary in your imaginary safe house whenever you get scared. Whenever your brain senses you are in danger (read: a mild, medium or spicily stressful situation) it responds by impulsively wanting to fight, flee or freeze. Here are three things you can do to regain composure and boost your energy the next time you find yourself cowering.

1 Know you are safe. Pay attention to what is happening in your body and in your mind. If you feel like you're having a heart attack or think you're going mad, calm yourself by saying something like 'I'm medically safe. This is just a response to this situation', and repeat it until you feel better.

2 When you are freaking out it is difficult to just snap out of it, but with awareness you can switch on your relaxation response. Deep breathing and exercise will always get the endorphins pumping through your body.

3 Pay attention to the present moment and try to disassociate what's happening, rather than relating your experience to a past problem or future fear.

WHEN TO DO IT

Frequently. The more your brain senses risk, the more often it responds in similar ways, so with practice you can move past your troubles the next time they try to trip you up in this way.

TOP **FIVE** WAYS
to turn on the light

Accept yourself and
others unconditionally

Learn to distinguish reality from fantasy

Ditch unnecessary, energy-sapping,
psychological baggage

Respond to situations in a mature and
emotionally intelligent way

Find ways to explore your
creative capacity

27 NEGATIVE THOUGHTS

There is a fable about guardian angels: when someone says 'my life is awful', his or her guardian angel writes down 'awful life'. If the person says 'my job is boring' or 'my body is ugly', the angel writes 'boring job' and 'ugly body'. These angels are our subconscious minds and knowing this can make negative thoughts and emotions even scarier. Although you may never make them disappear completely, use this exercise to reduce their frequency and/or intensity, and help focus your energy on a bright future.

1 Knowing that your guardian angel is keeping track of everything you say to yourself (essentially writing the story of your life as you're living it), think positively about what you want him or her to know.

2 Try the counter technique: the next time a negative thought enters your mind, counter it with the opposite (positive) thought. For example, when you think 'I am going to make a fool of myself in front of those people', counter it with 'They are going to love me and give me a standing ovation'.

3 Try the delete technique. When an unwanted thought pops into your head, imagine you have a delete button that erases, obliterates, smashes or destroys it. Get creative and make it fun!

WHEN TO DO IT

If you deal with daily doom and gloom, this exercise may prove useful at any time of day. You can overcome anything if you put your mind to it.

28 METAL ENERGY

Even though many heavy metal musicians wear black and scream and growl, studies have shown this countercultural form of music and dance doesn't cause mental health problems. Quite the opposite, in fact. People struggling with anxiety and depression often find dancing a cathartic way of exorcising excess energy. So if you are mired in melancholy; flinging your hair around or bobbing your head to the beat might be just what you need to become energized again in a more positive way.

1 Let go of what you think metal is. Many metal musicians are highly trained and influenced by classical, jazz, opera and folk music.

2 What styles of music do you prefer? Faster or slower? Male or female vocals? Guitar solos or beating drums? Any lyrical themes that soothe your soul? Find a blog about metal, describe your preferences and ask for suggestions on what to listen to. Don't be scared; fans of all styles of music are friendly.

3 Explore. Watch videos or go to a show. You don't have to go hair-flinging or head-banging your way into a mosh pit – unless you really want to, that is.

WHEN TO DO IT

If other forms of emotion-ejecting therapy have failed you, try music and dance. This hallowed harmonic duo of rhythm and rhyme has been helping people expel their demons for eons.

29 YOU, SUPERHERO

We see superheroes flitting here and there, flaunting their super strength with volunteer spirits, but why are we so drawn to the action and adventure that eclipses and upstages our own wildest dreams? Because we all have a superhero hiding inside us! We just keep our costumes and capes hanging in the back of our wardrobes where we think they belong. But remember: superheroes weren't born super (most began as humble humans), so if you want to play the role that was written for you, follow these five steps to start accomplishing fabulous feats of your own.

1 Seek out every opportunity to develop your strengths. Compensate for your weaknesses by finding people who play at what you have to work at.

2 Crush your fears. People cower from fright because they are afraid. Can you imagine Batman slumping in his chair and sighing when the bat phone rings?

3 Follow your heart as if your life is a cliché, because you have a choice every second of every day where to direct your energy. What will you focus on?

4 Ask questions to get to the root of the problem/opportunity. Put your nano-powered noggin to work for you and get some answers.

5 Be willing to overcome obstacles on the road less travelled. You will find the gold not at the end of the rainbow, but likely veiled in mist and obscured by rain.

WHEN TO DO IT

It can be hard to believe you are super(b), yet all the energy you need to succeed can be coaxed out of the wardrobe and celebrated into existence any time you feel like it.

30 SET YOUR SHADOW FREE

Shadow work refers to the process of discovering and welcoming the aspects of our personalities we don't like back into our lives. When conducting this illuminating work, it's important to let go of judgement or criticism, both of which cloud understanding. Be compassionate, patient and go easy on yourself, because peeling onions makes most people cry. Looking under the bed is scary and uncomfortable, which is why most people never even think to do stuff like this. If only they knew the power of the dark side! You will get the most out of this process based on psychologist Ken Wilber's work if you don't let temporary discomfort get in the way of putting a sprightly bounce back in your step.

1 Pick a person in your life who regularly stirs your emotions, either negatively or positively; a person who irritates or upsets you, or someone you find attractive and irresistible.

2 Describe the qualities in this person that upset you or entice you the most, referring to them in the third person (he, she, it). Either speak out loud or write your findings down in a journal. Don't hold back or worry about saying the wrong things. Express yourself. The person in question will never know you did this exercise.

WHEN TO DO IT

You can climb the ladder of enlightenment after every emotionally charged interaction if you like. There is no end to what psychic treasures you can unearth when you sharpen your shovel and start digging. (P.S. You can't dig too deep.)

3 Now pretend to have a conversation in your imagination. Speak to the person using 'you' language, as if they were standing in front of you. Tell them everything that bothers you (or that you love) about them.

4 Ask questions like: Why are you doing this to me? What do you want from me? What are you trying to show me? What do you have to teach me? Then wait for your imaginary friend to respond. Either speak for them yourself, out loud, or record the exchange in your journal.

VERY IMPORTANT

There are no quick fixes in shadow work. You will not see your life change overnight. Give the processes the attention and time they require and you will see the benefits and blessings blossoming into your life.

5 Now morph into this person. Make their fascinating qualities yours using first-person language (I, me, mine). This will feel awkward, but don't worry; it's exactly how it should feel. You have these button-pushing traits inside you too (you've just been denying their existence). Say things like: 'I am jealous' or 'I am radiant'. Fill in the blanks with whatever you find: 'I am _____'.

6 Fully experience what it's like to be this person; to live and act and think and feel how they do, and you will quickly integrate these qualities and essentially become a more whole human being with greater capacity for compassion, kindness, patience and understanding.

PERSONAL AFFIRMATION

I set my shadow free

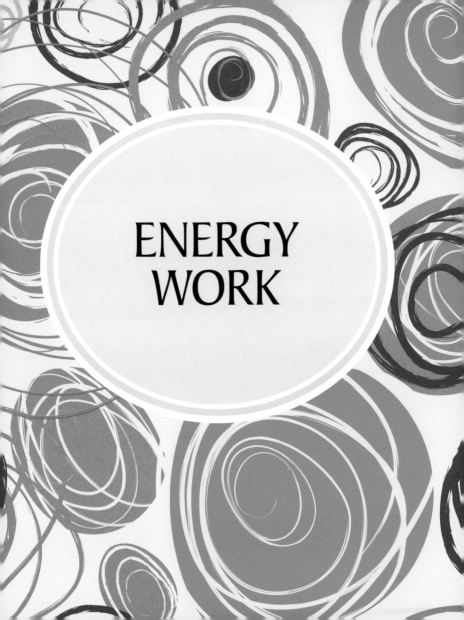

ENERGY
WORK

Humans are engines of energy, full of celestial-sent creativity just waiting for the spark of awareness to ignite it. Energy is everywhere. Every culture has studied it in some way for thousands of years. Not only are we superhighways of energy itself, but we also travel in and on and with it, as we ebb and go with the flow like bullet trains headed everywhere all at once at light speed.

In this chapter you will be guided to focus your energy and put it to good purpose, and to promote and sustain a state of abundant, vibrant health and life-lasting wellbeing. All you have to do is hitch a ride on the frequencies of love, light and limitless ability and become an alchemist who transforms lead into gold.

You are not alone in your journey; there are teachers and healers and mentors to guide you, and when you open your heart and your head, you will be drawn to them, and they unto you. May you exude endless effervescence for all to feel, for this is your birthright, an inheritance you earned the day you were born.

31 FEEL THE CHI

Tai chi is a gentle, centuries-old Chinese martial art that sustains your energy by calming, centring and conserving it. These natural, low-impact movements merge with meditation, resulting in a happy marriage between mind and body. Practising these meditative movements will help you relax, improve your balance, increase your flexibility, contribute to a better night's sleep and perhaps even prolong your life.

1 Pick your preferred style (there are five to choose from). The most popular is the Yang style, which includes 108 sequences of movements (there are 108 pressure points in the body). Each movement has five or six parts, each flowing easily into the next.

2 Choose your class. Feel free to ask questions of the instructor before joining, keeping in mind that 2,000 years' worth of knowledge takes a lifetime to study, practise and master.

3 Go outside. You will often find tai chi practitioners communing with nature in parks close to community centres and residential homes. Join them in breathing fresh air while tenderly tensing and releasing your muscles under a gentle sun or cool cloud cover.

WHEN TO DO IT

Gurus recommend spending 20 minutes a day, at least three days a week, to get the most out of your (meta)physical practice. It's safe and fun, so why not give it a try?

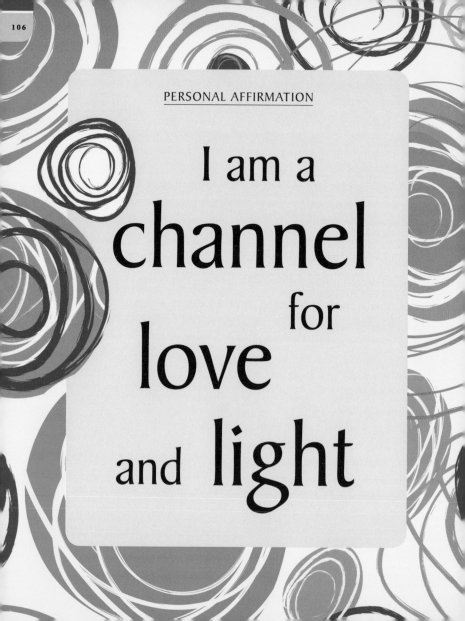

I am a channel for love and light

32 ENERGY HEALING

The spiritual belief that we are all connected via an invisible force that governs our mental, physical and emotional wellbeing was developed into a healing therapy called reiki by a Japanese Buddhist named Mikao Usui more than a century ago. When our energy ebbs, we don't function at our best; when it flows, so do we. Reiki is not a religious practice – anyone can realign their chakras in this way.

1 Close your eyes, take a few deep breaths until you feel relaxed and invoke the healing energy by stating your intention in summoning it.

2 Imagine a stream of healing white light flowing into you from above your head, into your heart, down your arms and out through your hands.

3 Imagine you are a channel for this bright healing light and direct it towards any part of your body it wants to go. Visualize the white light flowing through those parts of your body that need healing the most.

4 Once you feel the session is over, step back and express your gratitude by thanking the energy for the opportunity, guidance and healing.

WHEN TO DO IT

This therapeutic style of worship is available to you 24/7/365. If you used to go to church, but don't any more, and you miss it sometimes, do it every Sunday morning.

INITIATE THE FLOW

Don't be tempted to skip step 1. You must always initiate the flow of healing energy before beginning a reiki session.

33 TAKE A BREAK

Is there anything more energy depleting than sitting still in one place for hours on end without moving? Even if your work requires that you sit at your desk all day, you don't have to drain your batteries and slow your metabolism to a slug's slimy crawl. Flick on the trickle charger! According to cognitive behavioural therapy, physical activity is a crucial ingredient in maintaining clear thinking and a positive outlook. This exercise will supply both your brain and your body with the oxygen they need to get your work done and keep you from shutting down midway through it.

1 If you have been sitting for longer than an hour, take a deep breath, make a circle with your shoulders and move your head from side to side. Feel the stiffness in your neck, the dryness in your eyes, the loss of feeling in your legs and perhaps the fog rolling into your brain.

2 Now imagine someone standing behind you – either an energetic version of yourself on a Friday afternoon or a fidgety colleague counting the seconds until his or her next break.

3 Pretend this person spins your chair around and says, 'It's break time'. Leap out of your chair and make your way to the nearest exit.

WHEN TO DO IT

Practise this exercise whenever you have been sitting for a long time and your energy is going the way of the dodo bird.

A NEW HABIT

The more you do this, the more your body and brain will start to crave these mini breaks, having noticed the restorative effects.

4 If there is a park or community garden nearby, head straight for it, walking briskly but at a comfortable pace.

5 When you enter the park, notice the sun peeking through the leaves in the trees or the sounds of the birds singing sweet songs.

6 Pick up the pace a little and feel the breeze on your face as you return to the land of the living, your mind becoming sharper and your blood returning to your body.

7 You can now return to work feeling spry and spirited, being sure to notice the impression your rear left in your chair when you were fusing with it earlier.

8 Make a commitment to yourself that you will not fuse with your chair, and instead take a few 'mini breaks' each day.

9 Next time you make your way outside for a refreshing reset, ask one of your colleagues to join you. When it comes to meetings, you will find walk-and-talk sessions productive.

10 If you can't leave the office, at least leave your desk and find a quiet space to visualize your last park visit as you colour in the image opposite.

34 LIFT THE SKY

Back in the day, routine qigong exercises weren't enough for the devout
Buddhist and Taoist monks who were deeply committed to self-discipline.
They wanted to amplify their energy reserves and strengthen their internal
organ systems more than was possible with elementary qigong exercises
being practised by the unsophisticated folk at the time. Learning to
manipulate the *qi* (chi, or life force) led to the traditional belief that monks
could extend their life span to 150 years or more. If you'd like to increase
your chances of living longer, try this popular qigong exercise.

1 Keep your feet a few centimetres apart, point your toes and nose forward, relax your shoulders and rest your hands by your side. Spread your weight evenly. Relax your jaw and close your mouth only when you need to swallow.

2 Arc your arms up slowly, breathing in gently through your nose as it follows your hands. You can close your mouth as you inhale. Relax and close your eyes once you get the hang of it.

3 When your hands are above your head, push up gently, as if you are lifting the sky with your palms. Stretch but keep your shoulders relaxed. Keep your heels on the floor and your nose pointing towards the sky. Don't struggle. Stay soft.

4 Bring your arms down slowly like a bird lowering its wings and breathe out gently as if you are steaming up a mirror, but gentler. Each movement should be fluid, flowing into the next. Repeat.

WHEN TO DO IT

Get into the habit of practising lifting the sky for two minutes every day and see if you can do it for 30 days in a row (that's only one hour a month).

35 STAND TALL

From feeling pain to believing in yourself, your posture influences more than you give it credit for. Improving the health of your spine will provide pose for years to come. This exercise will twist your joints and bones into alignment and activate and strengthen your abdominal muscles so you can maintain correct posture (and your energy levels) whether you're standing or sitting. Whenever you sit, your feet should be flat on the floor, your shoulders 'back but relaxed', your ears above your collarbones and your back as straight as possible. When you stand, your legs should be slightly bent, not locked.

1 Sit down comfortably on the floor and bend your legs at the knees.

2 Lifting both feet at the same time, raise them about 15 centimetres off the floor.

3 Tense your core (tummy) muscles and rotate your upper body from left to right.

4 Lower both feet gently to the floor and repeat the exercise.

WHEN TO DO IT

Practise this muscle-strengthening exercise whenever you notice your energy spiking or subsiding, and it will eventually become a healthy habit.

36 WALK WITH ZEN

Walking is wonderfully therapeutic and Zen is zeroed-in transcendent. Put the two together and you get more calorie-burning energy, greater weight loss, improved sleep, lower blood pressure and fewer sick days (a study showed walking for 20 minutes a day, five days a week resulted in 46 per cent less time off due to illness. So put on your shoes, sandals or army boots and head for the door. This calmly energizing Buddhist meditation technique, which could be referred to as mindful walking, will relax your body and liberate (silence) your mind, the greatest barrier to spiritual freedom.

1 Make your way to a favourite park, path, garden, or labyrinth.

2 Make a fist with one hand and lightly lay your other hand on it.

3 Begin to walk, focusing on how your feet and legs feel. Notice what each step feels like, and become aware of what your mind is thinking about what you're doing. If you look carefully, you will notice the connection between intent and action. Contemplate this.

4 Study your surroundings with your senses. Smell the air, feel the wind, marvel at the colours around you and listen.

5 Go at a comfortable pace and count each step if this helps you focus. The more time you spend walking in a Zen way, the slower your stride will become.

WHAT TO DO NEXT

After becoming a Zen walking master, try some of the similar mindful movement exercises in this chapter, such as Feel the Chi (page 105) and Lift the Sky (page 112).

TOP **FIVE** WAYS
to keep your energy flowing

Practise your favourite form of exercise
every day (even just a quick stretch)

Focus on what you love and refrain
from thinking about what worries you

Lovingly let go of energy 'eddies'
by going with the flow

Spend time with positive people
who inspire you

Remember to breathe

37 FILL IN THE GAPS

No doubt you already know that eating oxidant-fighting superfoods such as dark chocolate, wild salmon and kale will give you more vim and vigour. But are you also aware that your body can crave vitamins and minerals in its bid to keep your energy levels up? Here is a list of five supplements to fill those all-important gaps in your gut and give you some much-needed get up and go.

1 When you don't have enough magnesium in your body, your cells can't produce the energy you need to get through the day. If you feel sluggish, magnesium might mean the difference between an afternoon boom or bust.

2 Iron produces haemoglobin, which keeps oxygen moving through your bloodstream. It's an absolute must for manufacturing energy. If you aren't eating enough meat or vegetables, you might not be getting enough to maintain your energy levels.

WHEN TO DO IT

Supplement your diet according to your healthcare provider's guidance and recommendations.

3 Related to iron, your body not only relies on vitamin B12 to produce healthy red blood cells, it also needs it to properly digest, absorb and synthesize protein, carbohydrates and fats. Many people say this B puts the pep in their step.

4 Although folic acid also helps produce red blood cells, it is destroyed during the cooking process, which means people generally don't get enough of it. Take it with B12 to benefit the most.

5 Your brain is 80 per cent water. When you are dehydrated, your heart not only has to work harder to supply your body with all it needs, your body also can't cool down as easily (which leads to a variety of symptoms including the enemy of energy: fatigue). Drink some.

38 TAP IT OUT

Also known as 'tapping' or 'psychological acupressure', the emotional freedom technique (EFT) is believed to relieve the pain of negative emotions. While acupuncture uses needles to apply pressure to these points in the hope of restoring the flow of energy in our bodies, the emotional freedom technique works with your fingertips. It has been known to reduce both anxiety and insomnia.

WHEN TO DO IT

Practise this peculiarly pleasurable procedure whenever possible to put an end to your problems.

BE PATIENT

If tapping your troubles away doesn't work at first, simply repeat the sequence to lessen their intensity. You will eliminate them altogether eventually.

1 Identify one problem that will be the focus of your tapping and define it with a phrase like 'Even though I have this [fear or problem] I deeply and completely accept myself'.

2 Define its level of intensity on a scale from 0 to 10, with 10 being the most difficult. This will help track your progress.

3 Recite your phrase and tap each of the eight meridian points of your body eight times: top of head; eyebrow; side of either eye; under each eye; under the nose; chin; collarbone; under your arm.

4 At the end of the sequence, rate the intensity level of your issue. If you're not at 0, do it again until you get there.

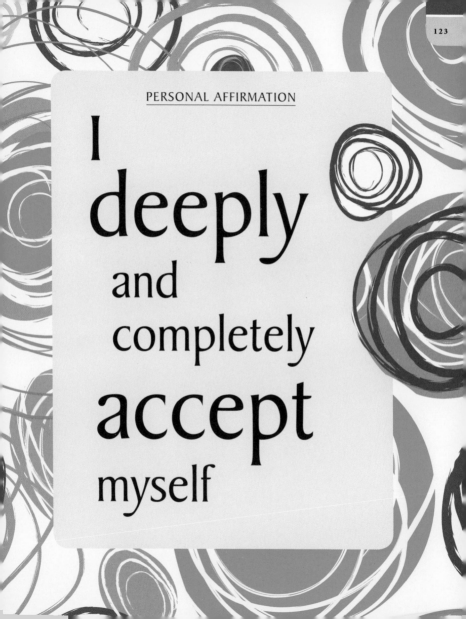

PERSONAL AFFIRMATION

I deeply and completely accept myself

39 DANCE IT OUT

Did you know sweat is the best antidepressant on the market? It's also free. If you find you are often misunderstood by people because they don't appreciate the difference between your wants and needs – like, you want abs, but you need ice cream – and you consider the thought of playing any sport more harmful to your health than two scoops of chocolate chip cookie dough, there is still hope, unless you don't like music, of course. If you believed in Father Christmas for eight years, you can believe in yourself for three to five minutes (the length of an average song), so get down and bust a move like it's 2999. Here's how:

1 Go home, move the furniture, draw the curtains, turn off the lights, crank the stereo and rock out!

2 If you find you were born with two left feet and are getting self-conscious, just remember that no one is watching (nor would they want to).

3 Have fun. Some people believe that moving to music is the second-best recreational diversion on the planet.

WHEN TO DO IT

Cut up a rug whenever Saturday night feels far away.

40 BREATHE FIRE

This healing Kundalini yoga meditation technique not only wakes up your nervous system, cleanses your body, heightens your awareness and increases your powers of observation, but it also jacks up your energy and endurance. Studies have shown this practice makes it easier to recover and relax after strenuous exercise by reducing lactic acid build-up in your body. As you breathe in and out briskly but rhythmically (like a panting dog), your diaphragm becomes a bellow for your fireplace, oxygen fuelling your inner fire and energizing body, mind and spirit.

1 Sitting with your spine straight, rest your palms on your knees and take a few slow, deep breaths to relax your body.

2 Start 'panting like a dog'. Take short, quick in-and-out breaths, ensuring each in and out lasts the same amount of time. The inhale is passive and the exhale is powerful.

3 Once you get the hang of it, start breathing through your nose and quickening (though continuing to equalize) the pace. Go slow if you want; it's not a race.

4 After about 30 seconds, slow down your breathing and stop exerting yourself. You may feel your body tingle and notice a slight glow.

5 Gradually increase the time you spend on this exercise and you will eventually become a fire-breathing dragon!

WHEN TO DO IT

Whenever you are feeling blah (like around 3 pm every day), skip the espresso and breathe fire to trick your brain into believing you just ran around the block.

HEALTH CHECK

If you suffer from vertigo, spinal disorders, cardiac problems or are pregnant, have asthma, a respiratory infection or high blood pressure, do NOT practise this exercise.

MIND OVER
MATTER

According to cognitive behavioural therapy, our thoughts are responsible for our countless problems. In our helpless state, we seem to summon endless evidence for how we and other people should behave, and how life ought to treat us. Luckily for you, you can change your thoughts, and thus the direction of your life, as long as you don't get stuck in pain and suffering. Try to see that, although pain is inevitable, suffering is optional. Claiming ownership of your unlimited storehouse of potential only becomes possible when you prevail over your illusory interpretations of matter, and learn to see the truth.

In this chapter you will learn how to harness and direct the unstoppable power of your magnificent mental muscle, and then learn to enjoy it with all the pizzazz you can muster. You will be able to turn your brain on or off at will, and wish all your whims into existence, for your brain is like a wind-up toy marching to its own drum. All you need to do is give it the instructions you want it to follow and point it in the right direction.

41 GET SMART

For any self-help programme to be effective in energizing and empowering you, it must follow tried-and-tested guidelines. Approaching goal-setting in this way will help you stay the course and get where you want to go. Identify your goals, and see if you can pinpoint what prevents you from following through in your quest. Put your goals into this S.M.A.R.T. framework and use them as your roadmap to your desired destination.

1 Specific. What do I want to accomplish? Why do I want to achieve it? Who is involved?

2 Measurable. How do I know I have reached my goal? What do I imagine the steps to be? How will I track my progress?

3 Achievable. Have others achieved similar goals? Do I have the resources and skills I need? What am I missing? How can I fill any gaps?

4 Relevant. Is the goal within reach? Is it aligned with my values and relevant to the purpose of my life? Can I commit to achieving it?

5 Timely. Does my goal have a start and target date? When are they?

WHEN TO DO IT

Without goals we are like sailing boats without sails, so feel free to sit down and conduct S.M.A.R.T. goal-setting sessions whenever you feel the need to correct your course.

42 REFRAMING EMOTIONS

Some beliefs are harmful and destructive to our overall wellbeing and thus sap our energy and enthusiasm for following the footpath to bliss. The good news is we can restructure, rescript, reframe and/or replace our emotions. Use this exercise to help you regulate your emotions if you battle with debilitating daydreams or haunting nightmares.

1 First, try progressive relaxation techniques, such as slowly relaxing yourself from head to toe with your eyes closed while breathing slowly and deeply. Feel free to listen to music or guided imagery.

2 If your negative thoughts persist, pick a recurring one and describe what you see, hear, feel, smell and taste. Write it all on a piece of paper. Include your thoughts and feelings or beliefs about yourself when you're having the dream.

3 Choose a different outcome that occurs *before* any bad things happen in the dream. Write a happy ending that will make you feel good when you 'wake up'.

4 Now write out your nightmare in full, being sure to incorporate your positive changes and your new ending.

5 From now on, every night before falling asleep, rehearse the new dream, and start visualizing it as often as possible throughout the day (especially if it's a daydream).

WHEN TO DO IT

When nightmares keep you from sleeping (or leaving the house) this exercise will help you change negative daydreams and nightmares into positive dreams.

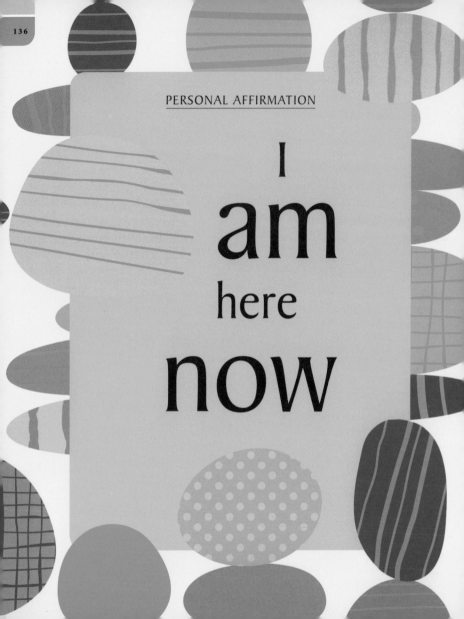

PERSONAL AFFIRMATION

I
am
here
now

43 TRANSCEND YOURSELF

What if you could alleviate anxiety and slash stress with the machete of your mind? Transcendental meditation (TM) may just be your cup of (green) tea, for this massage for your mind has assisted millions of mere mortals in achieving psychological harbour from the storm. Give it a try yourself. It might just let the wind out of your worries and sweep them out to sea permanently.

1 Sit comfortably in a chair with your hands on your lap and feet on the ground.

2 Close your eyes and take a few slow, deep breaths, then open up your eyes, close them, and keep them closed.

3 Repeat a simple Sanskrit mantra to yourself over and over again: 'I am' or a variant of this. When you start thinking about something else, return to repeating your mantra.

4 After about 20 minutes, wiggle your fingers and toes and return to earth.

5 Open your eyes and take a few moments to enjoy yourself before getting on with your day.

WHEN TO DO IT

Practise this meditation for 20 minutes twice a day, at times when you want to relax, be more productive or wish to sleep better. Once you see the benefits it brings, you will look forward to your next session.

44 EXPLAIN IT!

Anyone can read a book, watch an educational video or go to a seminar, but not everyone can explain what they learned, which is why this exercise is so effective in magnifying your ability to pay attention and concentrate. Explaining something to yourself not only helps you retain, reframe and reshape information you want to absorb; it helps you become a better listener, more creative thinker and passionate lifelong learner.

1 Talk to yourself. Slowing down to think about thinking allows us to learn more from an experience.

2 Ask why? Give the reins to your innate curiosity and you will be led beyond horizons. And when you hit solid rock, start up the jackhammer and dig up some answers.

3 Summarize. The art of summing up an idea and describing it in your own words will leave you with a better understanding of what you learned.

4 Connect the dots. Seeing associations and relationships between materials, concepts and theories will create cognitive links and inscribe the information onto your cerebrum.

WHEN TO DO IT

Whenever you are studying a subject and don't feel you've quite 'got it', explain it to yourself until you do 'get it'.

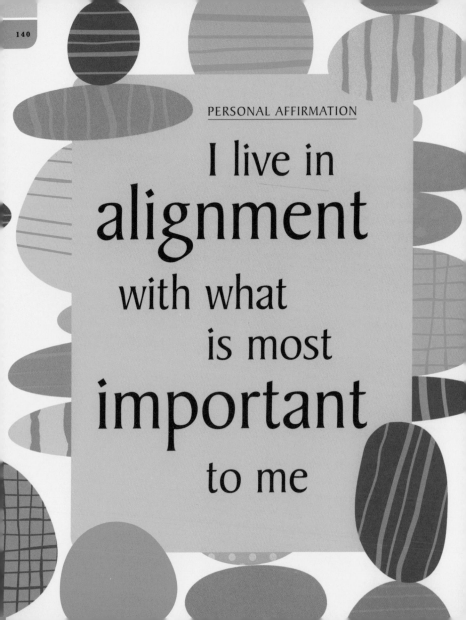

PERSONAL AFFIRMATION

I live in alignment with what is most important to me

45 AIM FOR THE BULL'S-EYE

Our values are a reflection of our heart's deepest desires. They guide us in our interactions with people, in making choices about what we do every day and in directing our energies to the things we care about most. In this eye-opening exercise based on psychologist Tobias Lundgren's work in cognitive behavioural therapy, you will see a dartboard divided into four areas that you need to fill in. As you follow the steps, make sure your answers represent your values and not someone else's. Getting married might be a goal, but it shows you value love, affection and commitment. Taking your son or daughter to a baseball game may be a goal, but taking an active role as a parent may be the value. Use the steps 1 to 4 to help you consider what your values are.

1 Work and/or education: How do you treat the people with whom you spend the most amount of time? How do you like to be treated? What skills do you admire in others, and what skills would you like to acquire?

2 Play and/or leisure time: How do you like to have fun? And how can you have more fun? What do you like about your playtime, hobbies and creative pursuits? Who would you need to become to enjoy life more?

WHEN TO DO IT

Whether you see a therapist or help yourself, ideally this is the type of exercise that could be completed at least once a year, if not every few months, to help you track your progress to hitting a bull's-eye with every dart.

3 Relationships: Who do you love and care about? Why do you love and care about them? How do they express their affection and attention towards you? What could you do to fill your life with more positive relationships?

4 Health and personal growth: How do you express your gratitude and appreciation for your existence? What leads you to maintain (or improve) your health? And what do you believe is necessary to become a better person?

5 Now draw an X in each section of the dartboard, based on where your values sit in relation to 'I am living my life in alignment with my values' versus 'I am not living in alignment with my values'. Where are your darts? What are you aiming for?

BULL'S-EYE REVISITED

When you repeat this exercise, compare notes with yourself. You may find your values have changed. This can be revealing (and healing, once you realize how naturally you can adapt over time).

TARGET PRACTICE

Use the bull's-eye chart to record your answers. Take your time and think about each, and then describe your values in the spaces provided.

Work

Play

Relationships

Health

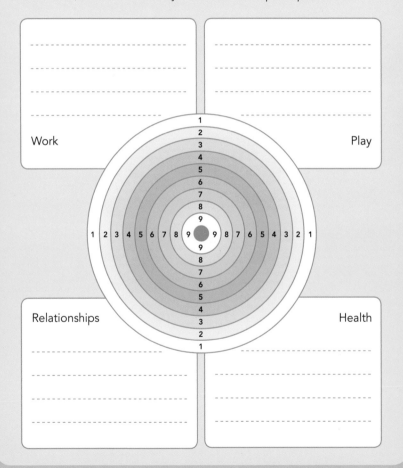

TOP **FIVE** WAYS
to exercise mind over matter

Acknowledge the healing
power of thought

Invest in your emotional intelligence

Remember that mental hygiene
and exercise are as rewarding as
physical exercise

Free yourself from limiting beliefs in
order to reach your potential

Let your thoughts help you achieve
magnificent goals

46 COMPASSION CHAIRS

A little like musical chairs – and much more effective because it can reconnect you with the underappreciated aspects of your personality – this exercise is based on the principles of schema-focused cognitive therapy developed by psychologist Jeffrey Young. According to Young, doing 'chair work' will enable you to address issues that affect you on a deep, subconscious level, allowing you to harness the potential energy of what you have been suppressing. The goals are clarity, perspective, wholeness and self-empowerment.

1 Arrange three chairs in a triangle and imagine self-criticism sitting in the first chair, the sensation of being judged in the second chair and a caring friend or trusted counsellor in the third chair. Your job is to be the voice represented by each chair.

2 Sit in chair no.1 and criticize yourself for something that has been bothering you. For example, 'I hate being lazy and not getting things done'. Listen to the tone and pay attention to what emotions you evoke. Check your posture, mood and attitude.

3 Now move to chair no.2 (the sensation of being judged) and say out loud what it feels like to be criticized in this way. For example, 'I feel hurt' or 'I don't feel supported'.

4 As before, notice your tone, feelings and posture, and then have a discussion (as Criticism and Sensation), doing your best to understand how each one feels.

5 Sit in chair no.3 (friend/counsellor) and with compassion, confront both out loud. What do you say? Get it all out.

WHEN TO DO IT

Negative self-talk will decrease over time as you practise speaking kindly to yourself. Give yourself time to express yourself from each perspective, and to reflect on the experience.

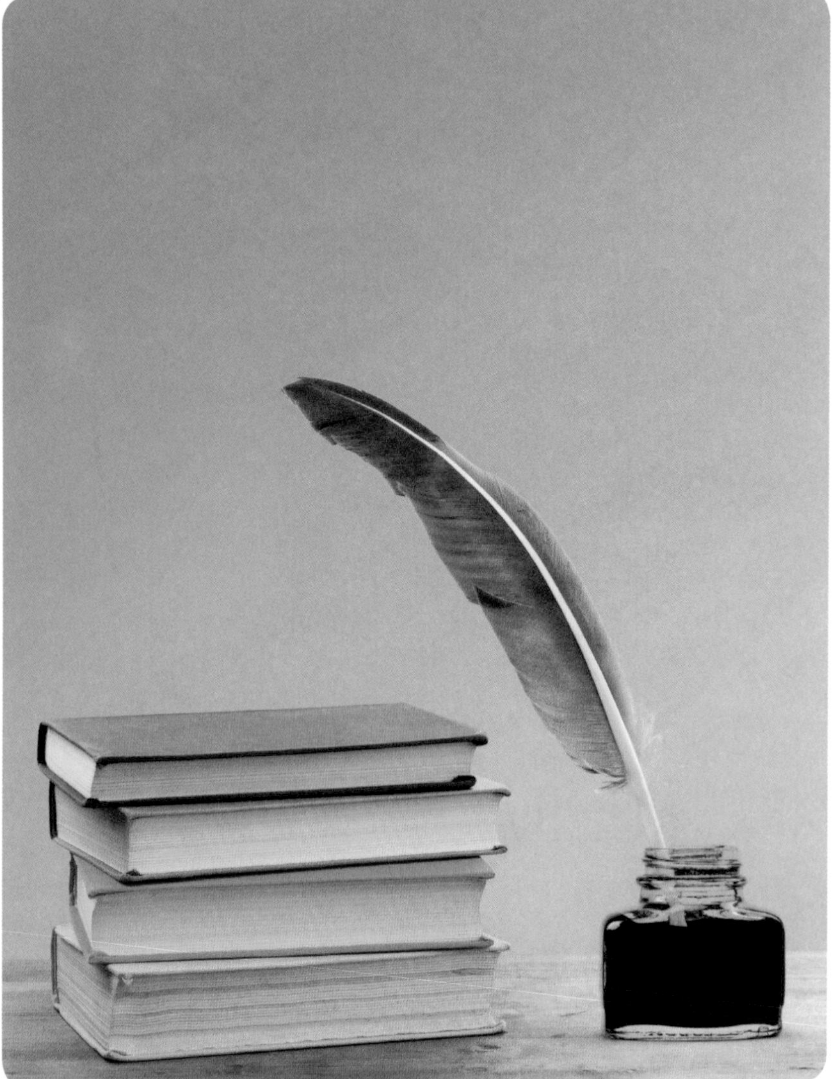

47 GRATITUDE JOURNAL

Gathering daily data describing your moods, where you think they came from, how long they lasted and how intense they were, is a common practice in cognitive behavioural therapy. But what if, instead of focusing on what is wrong, you record all the 'good' things that happened to you? This healthy, happy hobby can train your brain to concentrate on what makes you feel good and will bring clarity and energy into your life.

1 Spend time shopping for a special book that seems to say 'spend time with me!'.

2 Make it a habit. The easiest way to do this is to attach it to something else you do on a consistent basis, such as drinking coffee every morning or reading before going to bed.

3 Blank pages can be scary. Write three things your friends or parents or children did today. What are three ways to show appreciation without saying 'thank you'? Write about something you are looking forward to. You get the idea.

4 Don't force yourself to come up with new prompts; the more you practise reflecting on positive stuff, the more obvious entries will become.

WHEN TO DO IT

Whenever you set out to change a habit. It's good practice to check in with yourself every so often and notice if anything has changed. Are you happier or more productive? Have your relationships improved? Are you kinder to yourself?

48 MAPPING BY MEMORY

All cognitive activities, such as reading, reasoning and arithmetic rely on memory, of which there are several types grinding the gears of your grey matter. For your memory to do its job for the rest of your life it requires regular maintenance. Do you know your way around your neighbourhood with your eyes closed? Some people go gaga over globes and guidebooks, so you may find mapping your neighbourhood motivates you to get the lay of the land everywhere you go from now on.

WHEN TO DO IT

Any time you like. If you have ever wished you had gone into cartography, it's not too late to get into mapmaking.

GOT THE BUG?

If this activity was too easy, try drawing a map of your entire country and name every territory, region, state or county.

1 Get some coloured pencils and use the space opposite to draw a map of where you live.

2 Starting at your home, do your best to include all the major and minor streets, plus any local landmarks you have visited or know of.

3 Do this exercise from memory alone and resist any temptation to cheat.

4 When you've finished, pull out an established map and compare notes. How did you do? What did you miss? Are you surprised?

MY NEIGHBOURHOOD

Decide on whether you want to draw a portrait or landscape map and orient your page accordingly; choose a house icon you like the look of and copy it, placing it in a location to suit you, and get drawing.

49 PUT YOUR MIND INTO IT

'Get off your backside and put your back into it' is a common
admonishment of sadistic army sergeants and personal trainers hell-bent
on whipping your mind and body into shape. But fear not, for this exercise
is heaven-sent to help you exercise in a way that works for you. It takes less
than one hour, but the effects will likely last for months. A study conducted
at Columbia University found that participants who partook in a single
cognitive behavioural therapy session exercised twice as much as the
people who didn't. Here's how you can get the same benefits.

1 Spend some time reading an article or watching a video about the health benefits of physical exercise (30 minutes max).

2 Answer these three questions from the *American Journal of Preventative Medicine* and write down your answers. 1) What is my most important current wish regarding physical activity? 2) What is the most productive outcome of realizing my wish and events and experiences I associate with this positive outcome? 3) What is the most critical obstacle, together with events and experiences I associate with this obstacle?

3 Now comes what psychology professors call 'implementation intentions'. It's the most important step and could well mean the difference between following through and becoming a couch potato. Write your answers to these questions: 1) When and where does the obstacle occur, and what can I do to overcome or circumvent the obstacle? 2) When and where is an opportunity to prevent the obstacle from occurring, and what can I do to prevent it from occurring? 3) When and where is a good opportunity for me to act on my wish, and what would this action be?

WHEN TO DO IT

Repeat this process four times: twice to accomplish long-term goals in the coming weeks, and twice to achieve short-term goals in the next 24 hours.

50 BE YOUR OWN JUDGE

In cognitive behavioural therapy, the process of changing how you habitually think is called cognitive restructuring. It takes time, practice and patience. Given time, your moods will steady themselves and you will handle your ups and downs with ease. This exercise is a way of 'putting your thoughts to the test'. It is designed to help you slow down and stabilize your thinking (which leads to feeling), so you can regain a sense of cognitive equilibrium by bringing your mind and body back into balance and renewing your optimistic passion for life.

1 Describe a time you had a strong reaction, or wish you had reacted differently. Use the worksheet overleaf to record the facts: Where and when did it happen? Who was involved? What triggered the event?

2 Describe the emotions you felt at the time. They might include the following: depressed, anxious, angry, guilty, ashamed, afraid, happy (you can do this exercise for positive experiences too).

3 Now rate your feelings and moods on a scale from 0 to 100. Don't worry about being precise; just listen to your intuition.

4 List every automatic thought and image that pops up in regard to the situation. See if you can remember what was happening in your head just before your mood changed. Some examples of automatic thoughts include: 'I'm such an idiot', 'Nobody likes me', and 'This world is such a terrible place'.

5 Once you have compiled your list, try to recognize the thought with the most energy – that is, the one most hardwired to your mood – and circle it. This thought has been subpoenaed and will now have its day in court.

WHEN TO DO IT

Taking your thoughts and feelings to trial in this way should only be attempted when you have the necessary time and space available to devote your full attention to the process.

6 List supporting evidence for a case 'against' this thought, avoiding explanations and judgements. If your key thought is 'I'm such an idiot' following a minor mishap, these assertions could be considered reasonable: 'My mistake caused a delay', or 'I overlooked a detail'.

7 Generalized statements such as the following would not constitute plausible evidence: 'I ruined the whole day', 'I'm lousy with details'.

8 Now assume the role of prosecutor. There are probably holes in your story and it's your job to find them. Your evidence against 'I'm such an idiot' could look like this: 'I get things right more often than not', or 'I made a mistake in the morning, but I did a few things right after lunch'.

9 As the judge, you now get to weigh up both arguments and see if you can reach a verdict that is fair and unbiased. You may come to the following conclusions: 'Sometimes I make mistakes, but I am often careful and responsible', and 'I can improve based on what I've learned'.

10 Finally, rate your belief in each new thought from 0 to 100 and rate your moods again. Do you feel differently? What has changed?

FURTHER ACTION

Of course, there will be times when your main thought is 'I can't do this job' or 'This relationship is toxic'. If your conclusions are that you are unable to turn things around, this is a problem you need to solve.

ON TRIAL

Use this chart to put your emotions and thoughts to the test.

The incident:

Emotions:

Rating before and after the trial:

| 100 | 100 |
| Before | After |

Thoughts:

Evidence against me:

In my defence:

The verdict:

PERSONAL AFFIRMATION

If I take care of my mind, my mind will take care of me

ACKNOWLEDGEMENTS

Picture credits 2–3 and throughout Shutterstock/SAHAS2015; 6 Shutterstock/popovartem.com; 8 Shutterstock/Ivonne Wierink; 11 Shutterstock/Eakachai Leesin; 12/13, 25, 34, 42–43, 59, 62, 72–73, 78, 99, 100–101, 106, 123, 128–129, 136, 140, 158–159 Shutterstock/Elena Melnikova; 15 Shutterstock/Annette Shaff; 16 Shutterstock/Pavel Lysenko; 18 Shutterstock/iordani; 20 Shutterstock/5 second Studio; 26 Shutterstock/Atstock Productions; 28 Shutterstock/Hakan Tanak; 30–31 Shutterstock/Evgeny Atamanenko; 32 Shutterstock/Valeri Potapova; 36 Shutterstock/irur; 38 Shutterstock/Sue Martin; 45 Shutterstock/lovelyday12; 46 Shutterstock/golfyinterlude; 48 Shutterstock/Andrekart Photography; 50 Shutterstock/igorstevanovic; 52 Shutterstock/Lena Lir; 54, 138 Shutterstock/Sunny studio; 56 Shutterstock/Shaiith; 60–61 Shutterstock/Denis Kuvaev; 66, 68 Shutterstock/FabrikaSimf; 75 Shutterstock/Champiofoto; 76 Shutterstock/Papin Lab; 80 Shutterstock/Lukas Gojda; 84 Shutterstock/Kichigin; 86 Shutterstock/Alex Farias; 88–89 Shutterstock/Bee Seksan; 90 Shutterstock/Andrij Vatsyk; 92 Shutterstock/carlos castilla; 94 Shutterstock/YuryImaging; 96 Shutterstock/gu min; 103 Shutterstock/ PHOTOCREO Michal Bednarek; 104 Shutterstock/Svet_Feo; 108 Shutterstock/Twin Design; 111 Shutterstock/Nonuzza; 112 Shutterstock/Only background; 114 Shutterstock/Sergey Uryadnikov; 116 Shutterstock/Akura Yochi; 118–119 Shutterstock/Dark Moon Pictures; 120 Shutterstock/komkrit Preechachanwate; 124 Shutterstock/Voyagerix; 126 Shutterstock/Lindsay Helms; 131 Shutterstock/Mauro Rodrigues; 132 Shutterstock/Maciej Bledowski; 134 Shutterstock/Aleksandar Mijatovic; 143 Shutterstock/Canoneer; 144–145 Shutterstock/AppleZoomZoom; 146 Shutterstock/Alexander Prokopenko; 148 Shutterstock/Billion Photos; 151 Shutterstock/ArnaPhoto; 152 Shutterstock/titov dmitriy; 154 Shutterstock/BrAt82.

Cover: Shutterstock/SAHAS2015